This book belongs to:

_____

Should I Tell My Secret?

Talk About It Communications
info@collettesinnott.com
www.collettesinnott.com
www.talkaboutitcommunications.com

Special thanks to:

Carolyn Anderson	Kerri & Ceili	Mark Guimond
Susanne Heaton	Jolie Logan	Lucretia Martenet
Carolyn Pogue	Frankie Post	Gary Reid
Edward Ross	Erika Rowell	Darlene Sellitto
Kevin Sinnott	Laurie Szymanski	Dee Taylor

None of us get anywhere alone!

Should I Tell My Secret?

Silence ends by reading a story.

Dedicated to

My husband Kevin for all your love, support, and encouragement.

*My children Kohl, Ryder, and Jorja for your inspiration,
and the courage to talk about it.*

To all children,

May you laugh and play each and every day.

Talk About It!

Note to Parents

The purpose of this book is to help start the communication process between you, the parent(s), and your children in a way that is both encouraging and non-threatening. It is about a hidden subject that keeps a child isolated, confused and angry. I am a mother, and the survivor of sexual abuse. I realized that although I had lived the experience, I wasn't empowering my own children to know how to deal with potential abuse. I knew that if I, a survivor, was not talking about abuse with my children, then the likelihood that others were not was high. Way too high.

The story I am telling here may or may not reflect your exact circumstances. Your family make-up may be different, such as having only one parent, having both parents of the same gender, or having grandparents or legal guardians as parents. Of course, an offender may be someone other than an uncle. It could be any immediate family member, any relative, a family friend, or even the child's friend. It is almost never a stranger. Regardless of the differences, the essence of the story is the same.

We have the ability, opportunity and duty to empower our children. We do this by giving them the necessary information and education. We can accomplish this by simply planting the seeds of that information early.

So go ahead, it is never too early, nor too late, to Talk About It.

We can prevent child sexual abuse. One story, one conversation, one child at a time.

Yours in truth

There is a game within this book.

After reading the story, please go back through the pages and see if you can tell who on each page, including the cover, is sharing a secret. Can you find all the little characters who are whispering? There are 23 in total.

What kinds of secrets do you think they might be sharing?

_____

_____

Are they big secrets or little secrets?

_____

_____

How do you think each of them feels about telling or being told the secret?

_____

_____

Do you think they should tell someone else about their secret?

_____

_____

What do you think would happen if they did tell someone else their secret?

_____

_____

Would you tell someone your secret?

_____

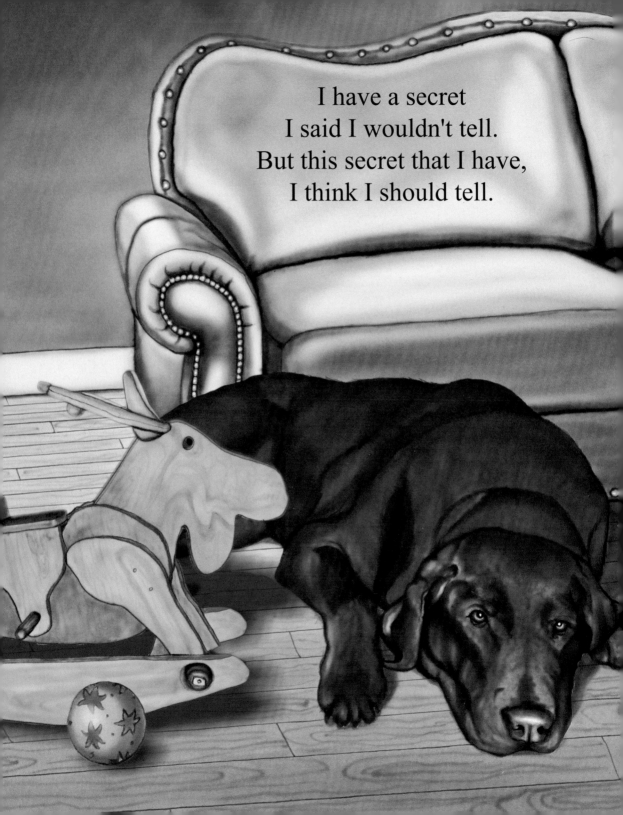

I have a secret
I said I wouldn't tell.
But this secret that I have,
I think I should tell.

"Mommy, can I tell you a secret?"
"Of course you can, Sam.
You can tell me anything."
"Okay but you can't tell anyone.
My friend Sarah would
be very mad at me."

"Sam, did you know that nobody, not a friend or even another adult, should ever ask you to keep a secret? If something makes you uncomfortable or sad or even mad, you should always tell someone. You can tell your mommy or daddy, or your teacher, even another mommy. You can tell anyone you feel safe with."

"Really?"

"Really."

"Sarah said her uncle Mike is spending a lot of time with her, and she likes that because he is her favourite uncle, but now he is playing a touching game. He touches her in places where her mommy said no one should. You know, private places, and she doesn't like it. She said he told her they have to keep it their little secret or bad things will happen."

"Oh Sam, I am so sorry that Sarah is going through this, and that you are confused. I promise you we will help her. You know, Sarah does not like that touching game, her uncle needs to stop. As an adult he should be keeping Sarah safe. By touching her in places that makes her feel bad, he is not. There are laws and that means there are rules to protect children from that kind of touching. It is not okay for anyone to touch you or anyone else in those places and in that way, ever! Did Sarah tell her mommy?"

"No, she said her uncle told her that her mommy and daddy would not believe her, and would be very mad at her, maybe not even love her anymore."

"Do you think that I would stop loving you if you were in her place?"

"No way! You love me no matter what, right?"

"Right. No matter what. And do you know why?"

"Why?"

"I love you, not because of anything you do; I love you just because you're you. So what do you think about this secret?"

"It makes Sarah sad, and that makes me sad. I think she should tell her mommy, like I told you."

"Well, I think we should go over to Sarah's house, because to help Sarah I need to tell her mom about this secret. And maybe you can talk to Sarah about why it is okay and important for her to tell her mom, okay?"

"Okay."

"Sarah, did you know that nobody should ever ask you to keep a secret?"

"Really?"

"My mom says that it is always okay to tell anything to anyone that you trust and feel safe with. And nobody, not a grown-up or a friend, should ever ask you to keep any kind of secret. I think you should tell your mom your secret, Sarah."

"But she will be mad at me and she won't believe me. What if she stops loving me?"

"I think she loves you no matter what. She loves you just because you're you."

"I don't know, I'm scared. He told me not to tell."

"Maybe if you tell your mom you won't be so sad or scared anymore. My mom says it makes you feel better to tell someone."

"Would you tell?"

"If something made me feel sad or mad like you are now, I would."

"What should I say?"

"My mom says to just say how you feel, and to tell the truth."

"Will you come with me to tell my mom?"

"Okay. What are best friends for?"

"Mommy, will Sarah be happy now?"

"In time she will be, because telling some-one is the first step to getting help. And because she has you for a friend."

"A best friend!"

"I am very proud of you, Sam. Sometimes it is hard to know what to do, but you always have mommy and daddy as well as other adults that you trust to help you. It takes someone very brave to share a secret. Thank you for sharing your secret with me."

"You're welcome, mommy,
I love you."

"I love you too, no matter what; I love you just
because you're you."

Now that Sam and Sarah have told their secret, they are able to laugh and play just like kids should, instead of worrying about keeping a secret. So if you have a secret that you do not like, it's okay to go ahead and...

Talk About It!

Worksheet

My list of people that I trust and feel safe to talk to.

_____   _____

_____   _____

_____   _____

_____   _____

_____   _____

_____   _____

_____   _____

Remember, if one person does not listen, tell someone else on your list.

These are all the little characters telling secrets.

Did you find all of them?